TERMINAT

CYBERNETIC

First published in Great Britain in 1996 by Boxtree Limited,
Broadwall House, 21 Broadwall, London SE1 9PL

A CIP catalogue entry for this book is available from the British Library.

ISBN 0 7522 0390 8

TERMINATOR™ 2: CYBERNETIC DAWN

BOXTREE

TERMINATOR 2

BOXTREE

PRESENT WAR

TERMINATOR 2 JUDGMENT DAY
CYBERNETIC DAWN

ABNETT · WHIGHAM · SNIDER

BOXTREE

DAN ABNETT • script
ROD WHIGHAM • penciller
JACK SNIDER • inker
DAVE LANPHEAR • letterer
MOOSE BAUMANN • color design
MALIBU • interior color
DAN SHAHEEN • editor
MARK PANICCIA • media line editor
story by DAN ABNETT & MARK PANICCIA with GERRY KLINE
cover by ROB PRIOR

TERMINATOR™ 2: JUDGMENT DAY

The Machines were our *legacy*, and our *curse*.

On August 29, 1997, they out-evolved us in the blink of an eye, and set about *manufacturing our extinction*.

But they underestimated humanity's resolve. They underestimated it then, and they underestimate it now.

Even when they resorted to time travel in a bid to erase our species...

...the Machines lost. Their future was crushed in a steel-press.

Their future melted in a blast-furnace.

I never asked for the responsibility of *preserving mankind*. It was forced on me, one night in nineteen eighty four, in a Los Angeles club called Tech Noir.

A voice said, "Come with me if you want to live," and my life as Sarah Connor, waitress, ended.

And my responsibilities began. Thirteen years before the eve of war. I've been fighting ever since.
Fighting for John, my only son. The human that the machines fear most of all.
The human who will defeat them.
They tried to kill him once, by killing me, before he was born. That was when I heard the voice.
It belonged to KYLE REESE. Voluntarily, he tumbled back through the years to protect me.
I will always love him. I see his scarred, noble beauty in John's face all the time.
And then tonight, ten years AFTER Kyle, the Machines struck again.
This time as a fluid thing. A shapechanger.
Together, John and I denied it. This time we fought alongside one of the machines, a re-programmed device that the adult John Connor, in years to come, would send back to safeguard our lives.
The thing I dread above all else.
A TERMINATOR.
Now dawn comes up and we've run as far as we can go.
I want to sleep. I want to sleep forever.
Enrique Salceda, Desert Gypsy, is an old ally.
He's sheltered me before. I pray he'll do it again.

ENRIQUE?
ENRIQUE? ¿PUEDE AYUDARME? ¿QUE PASA?
RR-CHAK
<GET AWAY! GET AWAY FROM HERE, BITCH FROM HELL! MY FATHER'S DEAD THANKS TO YOU!>*
*EDITOR'S NOTE--TRANSLATED FROM ESPAÑOL--DILAPIDATED DAN!
FRANCO! FRANCO, WAIT!
<YOU HEAR ME? GET AWAY!>

DROP IT, DICKWAD! CHILL OUT OR I SMOKE YOUR TEX-MEX ASS!
JOHN! NO!
WHAT THE HELL?
NO, JOHN, D --
-- UGHNNN!
M-MOM?
MOM!
M-MOM?
LO SIENTO, CHICO...
... I THINK SHE'S DEAD.
I hear the voice.
HIS voice.
DO YOU WANT TO LIVE? DO YOU REALLY WANT TO LIVE?
Then the heat. The light.
It burns my flesh, and it burns his beautiful voice away.
I want to cry, but my tears evaporate in the heat burst.
I know what this is. I KNOW WHAT THIS IS.

And then...
SARAH.

I CAME BACK ACROSS TIME FOR YOU.
I LOVE YOU. I ALWAYS HAVE.
KYLE!
IT HURTS. IT HURTS SO MUCH.

PAIN CAN BE CONTROLLED. YOU DISCONNECT IT.
I TOLD YOU THAT.

I HAD A PICTURE OF YOU.
I MEMORIZED EVERY LINE, EVERY CURVE...

...SO THAT I WOULD NOT MISTAKE YOU WHEN I FOUND YOU.
KYLE?
AHH!
NOOO!

SARAH CONNOR?
GET AWAY FROM ME!
GET AWAY FROM ME, YOU SON OF A BITCH!

Oh, GOD, PLEASE... NO MORE...
...NOT AGAIN... NOT AGAIN...

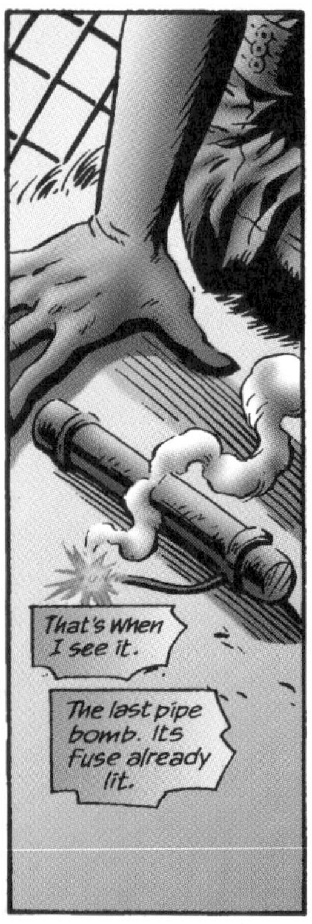
That's when I see it.
The last pipe bomb. Its fuse already lit.

SARAH?
NO! NO! NOOO!

THE FUTURE IS NOT SET. THERE'S NO FATE BUT WHAT WE MAKE FOR OURSELVES.
YOU KNOW THAT, SARAH CONNOR. SO WHY DID YOU HAVE TO KILL ME?
DYSON? DYSON ?!

FSSZ

NUUUH!
...oh, MAN.
YEAH, JUST LIKE THAT. LIKE SOME DEVIL.
MOM!
I'M OKAY.
FRANCO. I'M SORRY ABOUT YOUR FATHER.
WHAT IS IT YOU HAVE BROUGHT INTO THIS WORLD, CONNOR?
I don't know how to answer him. I listen as he tells me about Enrique, in a voice as dry as the desert...
...the motorcycle cop who rode in out of the night.
Who shrugged off bullets, and pinned his father to an ammo crate with a finger made from razor blades.
Who asked about John Connor.
GRENADES

He tells me about the curse Enrique spat...
...and the grenade.
And the blast that followed.
And the way the devil-cop stepped from the fire...
...and REASSEMBLED himself.
The polyalloy T-1000.
It came here looking for John and me, and Franco's father DIED rather than betray us.

So it turned on the children...
...it didn't kill them. It just asked them which way we went.

They didn't know any better. They were just scared. They pointed down the road.

AND THEN, IT THANKED US AND RODE AWAY.
CAN YOU BELIEVE THAT? IT THANKED US?

There's so much pain here, so much pain wherever I go.
Touching families, tearing them apart.
The Dysons, the Salcedas, the Voights, the Connors.

Sometimes I ask myself if it's worth going on.
Last night may have been the end, but I can't be sure.
And because I can't be sure, we'll never be safe. Not while there is a chance that SKYNET will still be born.

John and I are doomed to be victims, fugitives, outlaws...forever running, forever watching our backs and jumping at shadows.
And touching everyone we meet with our curse.

STEEL MILL, WILMINGTON.
...DETECTIVE WEATHERBY, L.A.P.D.
CAN YOU TELL ME WHAT'S GOING ON?
CSI STEEL
I'M AFRAID THIS MATTER IS NOW UNDER FEDERAL JURISDICTION, DETECTIVE. WHAT'S YOUR INTEREST HERE?
WE'RE LOOKING FOR AN ESCAPEE FROM PESCADERO, ONE SARAH CONNOR. SHE WAS INVOLVED IN THE FIRE-FIGHT AT CYBERDYNE LAST NIGHT, AND THAT TRAIL LEADS HERE.
FBI
POLICE LINE DO NOT CROSS
WISH I COULD HELP. I'M NOT AT LIBERTY TO COMMENT ON THAT.
YOU AND YOUR PARTNER HAD BETTER BE ON YOUR WAY.
BUT --
GOOD DAY, DETECTIVE.
DON'T TELL ME... THE FEDS AREN'T PLAYING NICE.
WHAT ARE WE SUPPOSED TO DO? FORGET IT?
THIS STINKS, MAN. I WANNA KNOW WHAT THEY'VE GOT IN THERE.
WITH ANY LUCK, IT'S THAT PSYCHO CONNOR IN A BODY BAG.
HEY, HEADS UP. CHECK OUT THE BABE.
SPASKY? I CAME AS FAST AS I COULD.
SORRY TO RUIN YOUR WEEKEND, KARYN, BUT YOU DO NOT WANT TO MISS THIS.
WHAT ARE YOU DOING?
IMPROVISING, BUDDY. GET READY TO MAKE THE MOST OF IT.

HEY, LADY! MAYBE YOU CAN HELP HERE. MOSSBERG, L.A.P.D.
WE MAY BE THE LITTLE GUYS, BUT WE DON'T INTEND TO STAND HERE FREEZING OUR NUTS OFF WHILE YOU GET TO HAVE ALL THE FUN!
I'M SORRY?
Oh, NOT AGAIN.
DETECTIVE, I TOLD YOUR PARTNER THIS WAS OUT OF YOUR JURIS-DICTION...
STATES
RNMEN
US 317
CAREFUL, FEDS. DON'T GET HIM STARTED...
POLICE
CROSS
...CAN YOU GET IT FREE?
GONNA TAKE SOME WORK. WHAT DID SPASKY SAY?
HE SAID WE SHOULD LIFT THE WHEEL RIGHT OUT, SO WE DON'T DAMAGE IT ANY FURTHER.
Oh, SURE...
Oh, MY GOD...

POLICE LINE
DO NOT
POLICE LINE
DO NOT CROSS
WHAT THE HELL IS THAT?
DETECTIVE WEATHERBY. DID YOU REALLY THINK WE WOULDN'T SEE THROUGH YOUR PARTNER'S TRANS-PARENT ATTEMPTS AT DISTRACTING US?
ESCORT HIM FROM THE BUILDING.
NOW WAIT A MINUTE...
YOU'RE LEAVING, MISTER.
AND I SUGGEST YOU REMEMBER THAT YOU HAVE SEEN ABSOLUTELY NOTHING HERE TODAY.
MAN! ARE YOU OKAY? WHAT HAPPENED?
WHAT DID YOU SEE? WEATHERBY?
WHAT DID YOU SEE?
DRIVE. JUST DRIVE.

MOM?
IT'S NEARLY TWO. SHOULDN'T WE BE MOVING BY NOW?
FRANCO'S TAKING HIS FAMILY SOUTH, SOME-PLACE NEAR SAUCILLO. ARE WE STILL HEADING FOR THE PLACE IN THE MOUNTAINS?
I GUESS.
SO, WHAT'S UP?
I WAS THINKING ABOUT DYSON. AND HIS FAMILY.
SHE MUST KNOW BY NOW. SHE MUST KNOW HE ISN'T COMING BACK.
YOU'RE NOT GONNA PULL SOME TRIP ON ME NOW, ARE YOU? SOME GUILT RIFF ABOUT THE PEOPLE WHO GET HURT ALONG THE WAY?
COME ON. THE TIME YOU SPENT TELLING ME WE CAN'T AFFORD TO CARE!
BUT IF IT'S OVER? CAN WE AFFORD TO NOW?
YOU WANT TO GO BACK, DON'T YOU? BACK TO SEE THEM.
AND WHAT WOULD YOU SAY TO THAT ?
IF IT IS OVER...
...THEN WE SHOULD.

Somehow, I expected him to talk me out of it. As usual, my son surprises me with his insight.
Perhaps that quality is what could make him so important one day.
55
With Franco's help, we pick up another car at a gas station and then say our goodbyes. I doubt we'll ever see the Salcedas again. For their sake, I hope we don't.
Logical strategy demands we go to ground in one of the bolt-holes I've prepped over the last decade.
But to do that would be to admit defeat. I don't want to think like that. I want to believe that last night at the mill, we turned destiny on its head and cast out the future that's been haunting us.
And if we believe that, then we have this hour of grace, a chance to make peace with the others who have shared in this bloodshed.
I NEED to do this. John knows it. I need to face down the ghosts and prove that fighting Skynet hasn't cost me my soul.
D'YOU THINK WE'LL HAVE TO WAIT FOR... YOU KNOW...
...JUDGMENT DAY...
...BEFORE WE'LL KNOW?
YOU MEAN, BEFORE WE KNOW IF WE WON?
I HOPE NOT.
I KNOW THIS MUCH, THOUGH... IF WE DIDN'T WIN...
...WE'LL FIND OUT PRETTY SOON.

MI VALLEY, CALIFORNIA.
Ms. STERN? THEY'RE READY FOR YOU.
NetWork DEVELOPMENTS
THANK YOU FOR COMING. I HOPE THE SHORT NOTICE HASN'T FOULED UP YOUR SCHEDULES.
PROCEED, PLEASE, Ms. STERN. I'VE GOT A FOUR THIRTY WITH THE GOVERNOR.
LATE LAST NIGHT, THE CYBERDYNE FACILITY IN IRVINE WAS INFILTRATED AND LEVELLED IN WHAT APPEARS TO HAVE BEEN A TERRORIST ACTION.
THERE WAS EXTENSIVE COLLATERAL DAMAGE AND A LARGE NUMBER OF LAW ENFORCEMENT AGENTS WERE INJURED.
THERE WERE ALSO SEVERAL FATALITIES, INCLUDING CYBERDYNE PROJECT CHIEF MILES BENNET DYSON.
THE VIOLENCE SPREAD TO THE FREEWAY, AND EVENTUALLY TO A STEEL MILL IN WILMINGTON, WHERE IT APPEARS TO HAVE CONCLUDED.
Mr. SPASKY AND I HAVE JUST RETURNED FROM WILMINGTON. WE MADE A DISCOVERY THERE WHICH WE'LL COME TO IN A MOMENT.
AS YOU KNOW, WE HAVE BEEN WATCHING CYBERDYNE'S RECENT WORK INTENTLY. AS A GOVERNMENT CONTRACTOR, THEY WERE OBLIGED TO PROVIDE THIS OFFICE WITH REGULAR REPORTS.
FROM THERE, WE KNEW THAT DYSON WAS CLOSE TO A GENUINE BREAKTHROUGH, ONE THAT WE HAD BEEN KEENLY ANTICIPATING FOR MONTHS.
CLASSIFIED

IS THIS YOUR WAY OF BREAKING BAD NEWS TO US GENTLY, KARYN?
NOT AT ALL, SENATOR.
I WON'T PRETEND DYSON'S DEATH ISN'T A SET BACK. AND WE LOST A GREAT DEAL OF VALUABLE DATA AND RESOURCES WHEN CYBERDYNE WAS RAZED.
IT'S THE CIRCUMSTANCES OF LAST NIGHT'S EVENTS THAT ARE PARTICULARLY INTERESTING, SIR.
WE RECOVERED A GRADE TWO LIMB SEGMENT FROM THE MILL. THERE SEEMS TO BE NO DOUBT THAT IT WAS TORN FROM A FUNCTIONING UNIT.
ARE YOU SAYING YOU'VE GOT A LIVE ONE AT LAST?
IT'S TOO EARLY TO TELL, MA'AM. WE'RE STILL SWEEPING THE AREA.
BUT I'M SURE YOU CAN SEE THE IMPLICATIONS--
NOT ENTIRELY, Ms. STERN. IT SEEMS TO ME THAT YOU'VE LOST MORE THAN YOU'VE GAINED. PERHAPS IT'S TIME TO REVIEW YOUR FUNDING AND--
WORST CASE, DYSON'S DEATH WILL SIMPLY SLOW THINGS DOWN A LITTLE. I'M FULLY CONFIDENT I CAN PICK UP WHERE HE LEFT OFF.
I HAVE COMPLETE FAITH IN KARYN'S ABILITY, MA'AM.
WE MIGHT JUST HAVE TO REVISE THE SCHEDULE. NOTHING MORE.

OKAY, BOTTOM LINE. WHAT CAN WE EXPECT TO SEE?
WE HAVE PEOPLE SCOURING DYSON'S HOUSE FOR ANY REMNANTS OF HIS NOTES. Mr. SPASKY IS ALSO DUE TO INTERVIEW DYSON'S WIDOW LATER TODAY.
AND THERE'S ANOTHER ELEMENT. PAGE SEVEN OF YOUR COPIES...
...THIS ONE CAME AT US FROM LEFT FIELD. HER NAME IS SARAH CONNOR. UNTIL YESTERDAY, SHE WAS A PATIENT AT PESCADERO STATE HOSPITAL.
I'VE RESEARCHED HER CASEFILE. SEEMS THAT FOR THE LAST DECADE, SHE HAS BEEN INSISTING THAT BOTH HERSELF AND HER SON HAVE BEEN TARGETS FOR TIME TRAVELLING CYBORGS.
SHE CALLS THEM "TERMINATORS."
IRONIC, ISN'T IT?
YOU'VE NEVER MADE THIS CONNECTION BEFORE?
TWENTY FOUR HOURS AGO, SARAH CONNOR WAS A PITIABLE, PARANOID FRUITCAKE.
SHE WAS AT CYBERDYNE AND WILMINGTON LAST NIGHT. SUDDENLY, WE'VE GOT TO TAKE HER SERIOUSLY.
FINDING HER IS OUR TOP PRIORITY.
WE COULD BE ON THE VERGE OF UNLOCKING GREATER SECRETS THAN WE EVER ANTICIPATED.
LADIES AND GENTLEMEN, WE'RE VERY CLOSE. AND, AS LAST NIGHT HAS SHOWN US...
...YOU NEVER KNOW WHAT MIGHT SHOW UP NEXT.

QUICK SHOP
I WAS THINKING.
THINKING WHAT?
SAY WE'VE *WON*, RIGHT?
WELL, THEN ... WE'VE STOPPED IT ALL FROM HAPPENING. BUT IF WE STOPPED IT FROM HAPPENING, WHY HAS IT *HAPPENED*?
JOHN?
I MEAN... IF WE WON WHEN WE *SLAGGED* THAT THING, WHY DIDN'T THE OTHER TERMINATOR DISAPPEAR?
WHY DIDN'T I DISAPPEAR?
I'M ONLY HERE BECAUSE REESE CAME BACK. HE ONLY CAME BACK BECAUSE THERE WAS *THAT* FUTURE TO COME BACK *FROM*.
THE FUTURE WITH SKYNET, I MEAN.
DOESN'T THAT MEAN THAT SKYNET IS GONNA HAPPEN *WHATEVER* WE DO?
I DON'T KNOW. REESE NEVER HAD TIME TO BRIEF ME ON THE CAUSE-AND-EFFECT OF TIME TRAVEL. I DON'T THINK *HE* REALLY UNDERSTOOD HIMSELF.
"ONE POSSIBLE FUTURE" HE CALLED IT. LIKE THESE WERE *ALTERNATE* ROUTES WE COULD TAKE...
MAX
... I GUESS IF THE FUTURE *ISN'T* SET, THEN THERE MUST BE ONE VERSION WHERE SKYNET *WILL* EXIST.
AND ONE WHERE WE *HAVE* WON.
LET'S HOPE THAT'S THE ONE *WE'RE* LIVING IN, HUH?

DINER
ALWAYS OPEN
...CAN'T YOU JUST LEAVE IT?
WHA' S'MATTER, YOU GOT A HOT DATE?
MAYBE I HAVE.
YEAH, RIGHT.
GOT NOTHING ON THAT JERK SPASKY. BUT THE BEEMER WAS REGISTERED TO A KARYN STERN...
THE BABE.
RIGHT, SHAKESPEARE. THE BABE.
SHE WORKS OUT OF A PLACE CALLED "NETWORK DEVELOPMENTS" IN SIMI VALLEY. BIG "N", BIG "W", IF YOU PLEASE.
PASS THE SWEET'N' LOW.
I GET YOU NOW! A DOLL LIKE THAT, A LOWLIFE COP LIKE YOU...HEY, IT COULD WORK!
WILL YOU GIVE ME A BREAK! I'M BEING SERIOUS HERE!
REAL SERIOUS. I KNOW WHAT I SAW TODAY. I KNOW THE FUSS THE FEDS WERE MAKING TO HUSH IT UP. AND I KNOW WHAT I'M THINKING.
AND IT SCARES ME, MAN. IT REALLY SCARES ME.
THAT CONNOR WOMAN MIGHT'VE BEEN TELLING THE TRUTH...

ROUTE 99 -- NEAR BAKERSFIELD.
...STILL STANDING, BETTER THAN I EVER DID, LOOKING LIKE A TRUE SURVIVOR, FEELING LIKE A LITTLE KID...
...STILL STANDING, AFTER ALL THIS TIME, PICKING UP THE PIECES OF MY LIFE WITHOUT YOU ON MY M—
SKZCZZZCH
SKZZCH
SKKZZKK
COME ON, YOU SUMBISH...
KASHOOK
WHADAF--?
FMMP

SKREEE
SKIIIK
SKREE
WHAT THE HELL HAPPENED?
GEEZ, MAN. I DUNNO.
LOOKED LIKE LIGHTNING HIT THE BLACK-TOP...
DID YOU SAY LIGHTNING?
YEAH. EVERYONE OKAY BACK THERE?
YEAH, YEAH... DID YOU SAY LIGHTNING?
HELLO EARL
HOLY MOTHER OF MERCY.
Oh, MY.

NEXT ISSUE:
SEARCH MODE

TERMINATOR 2

MALIBU COMICS #2

PRESENT WAR

$

TERMINATOR 2 JUDGMENT DAY

CYBERNETIC DAWN

PRIOR '96

ABNETT · WHIGHAM · SNIDER

"IT CAME LOOKING FOR HER, YOU SEE. AND GOD HELP ANYTHING OR ANYONE THAT STOOD IN ITS WAY.
"WEST HIGHLAND POLICE STATION, BACK IN '84. THAT WAS THE FIRST TIME. SEVENTEEN COPS DEAD, BUT YOU KNOW THAT.
"SEVENTEEN DEAD. SEVENTEEN. SEVENTEEN.
TERMINATOR® 2: JUDGMENT DAY
SEARCH MODE
Dan Abnett • writer
Rod Whigham & Gordon Purcell • pencillers
Jack Snider & Inker X • inkers
Patrick Owsley • letterer
Malibu Color • interior color
Mark Paniccia • line editor
Tom Roberts • color design
Dan Shaheen • editor
Rob Prior • cover art
• story by Dan Abnett & Mark Paniccia
HOMIC
"AND THEN LAST NIGHT, A DECADE LATER... IT CAME LOOKING AGAIN."

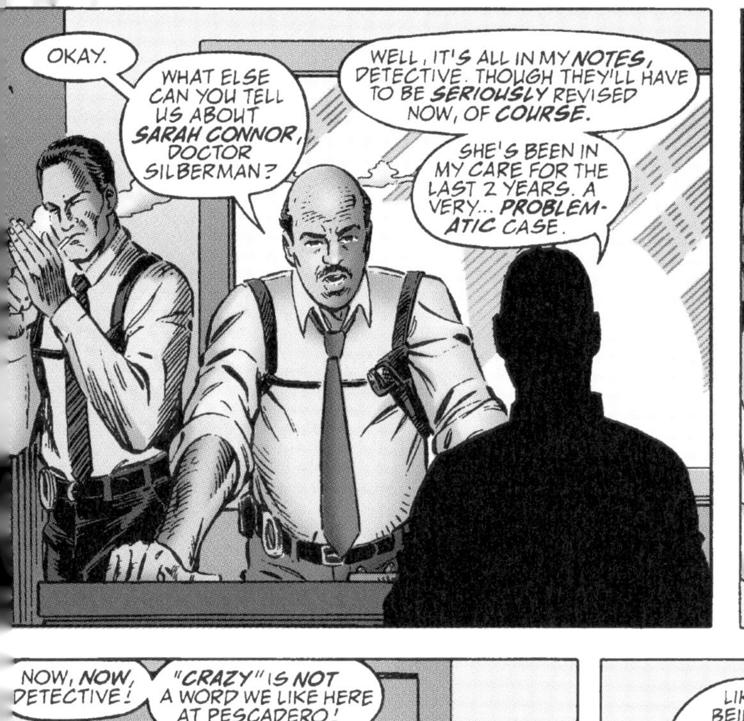
OKAY.
WHAT ELSE CAN YOU TELL US ABOUT SARAH CONNOR, DOCTOR SILBERMAN?
WELL, IT'S ALL IN MY NOTES, DETECTIVE. THOUGH THEY'LL HAVE TO BE SERIOUSLY REVISED NOW, OF COURSE.
SHE'S BEEN IN MY CARE FOR THE LAST 2 YEARS. A VERY... PROBLEMATIC CASE.

YOU MEAN SHE WAS CRAZY.

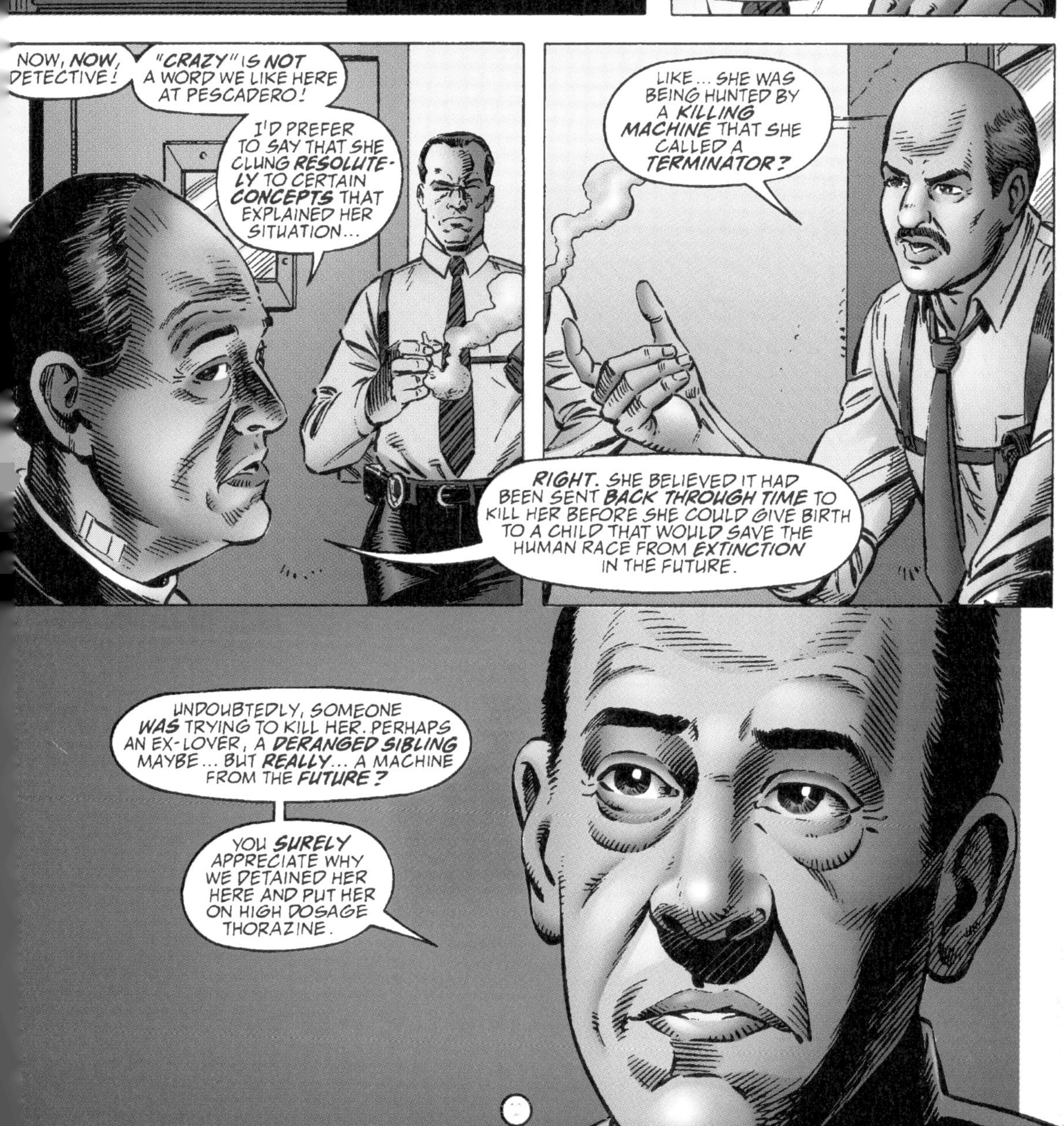
NOW, NOW, DETECTIVE!
"CRAZY" IS NOT A WORD WE LIKE HERE AT PESCADERO!
I'D PREFER TO SAY THAT SHE CLUNG RESOLUTELY TO CERTAIN CONCEPTS THAT EXPLAINED HER SITUATION...
LIKE... SHE WAS BEING HUNTED BY A KILLING MACHINE THAT SHE CALLED A TERMINATOR?
RIGHT. SHE BELIEVED IT HAD BEEN SENT BACK THROUGH TIME TO KILL HER BEFORE SHE COULD GIVE BIRTH TO A CHILD THAT WOULD SAVE THE HUMAN RACE FROM EXTINCTION IN THE FUTURE.
UNDOUBTEDLY, SOMEONE WAS TRYING TO KILL HER. PERHAPS AN EX-LOVER, A DERANGED SIBLING MAYBE... BUT REALLY... A MACHINE FROM THE FUTURE?
YOU SURELY APPRECIATE WHY WE DETAINED HER HERE AND PUT HER ON HIGH DOSAGE THORAZINE.

BUT AFTER LAST NIGHT?
WEEELLL... I'M CERTAINLY GOING TO REVIEW MY APPRAISAL OF HER DELUSIONAL ARCHITECTURE.
SO YOU GIVE CREDENCE TO HER STORY NOW?
WELL, NATURALLY!
DO I LOOK LIKE I'M CRAZY?
SO?
SO WHAT?
SO HE'S RAVING? SO THEY'VE GOT HIM ON HAPPY PILLS?
THINK I'D BE WEARING A BUTTON-UP-THE-BACK NUMBER IF I'D BEEN THROUGH WHAT HE WENT THROUGH LAST NIGHT.
I'M GONNA HATE MYSELF FOR ASKING THIS, BUT... YOU BELIEVE HIM, RIGHT?
PESCADERO
STATE HOSP
STATE OF CAL
IMINALLY DISORDERED
401
I DO.
I DON'T WANT TO...
...BUT I DO.

SOMEWHERE IN L.A....
HEY, HEY... CHECK THAT OUT!

LOOKS LIKE SOMEONE TOOK THE WRONG TURN!
LOOKS THAT WAY TO ME!
WHAT'CHA DOIN' HERE, YOU MOTHERS? YOUR RIDE BROKE DOWN?

SAID, WHAT'CHA DOING HERE, ASSHOLE?
THIS IS OUR TURF!
THIS-IS-OUR-TURF.
ARE YOU DISSIN' ME, JERK OFF?
BAMM!
BLAMM!
YEEEECHHK!

WASTE 'IM!
BAMM
BLAM
BLAMM
SHOOT 'IM DEAD!

BAMM
BAMM
THUK!
WHUKK!
THKK

UHKK!
AGHH!
HOLY SH-!
YOU ASKED FOR THIS BITCH! YOU ASKED FO--
SHHUKK
UHHKK-KK!

SHUNKK!
RRRR-CHAKK!

NEARBY...
WELL?
THEY'RE IN THERE, JOHN.
I JUST SAW DYSON'S WIFE AT A WINDOW. THIRD FLOOR.
DELIVERY
WE ARE GONNA GET SO BUSTED, TAILING FEDS ACROSS TOWN.
I'D BET REAL MONEY THEY SAW US WATCHING DYSON'S PLACE.
COME ON. YOU KNOW I'M BETTER THAN THAT.
THE FEDS HAD TO'VE MOVED THEM TO A SAFE HOUSE. STAKING THEIR HOME AND THEN FOLLOWING THE SUITS WAS OUR ONLY WAY OF FINDING THEM.
BUT YOU'RE RIGHT.
THE PLACE IS CRAWLING WITH GOVERNMENT PERSONNEL.
WE'RE GOING TO HAVE TO WAIT FOR AN OPENING

YOU'VE NO RIGHT! YOU'VE NO RIGHT!
PLEASE, MRS. DYSON... TARISSA...
DON'T CALL ME THAT, YOU EVIL SON OF A BITCH!
MOMMY? MOMMY? DON'T, MOMMY...
I'M SORRY! I'M SORRY, MRS. DYSON...
I CAN APPRECIATE THIS IS A DIFFICULT TIME FOR YOU, BUT WE HAVE TO RUN THROUGH THIS AGAIN...
WE DON'T HAVE TO RUN THROUGH ANYTHING, AGENT SPASKY! WE DON'T HAVE TO DO ANY DAMN THING WE DON'T WANT TO!
MY KIDS ARE SCARED. THEY WANT THEIR DADDY. AND HE'S NOT COMING BACK!
...MILES ISN'T COMING BACK...
EASY NOW, TARISSA...
MOM? DON'T CRY.
MOMMY?

DON'T YOU COME ON WITH THAT! DON'T YOU DARE!
OWK!
HUMMH.
OKAY, MRS. DYSON. WE'LL DO THIS LATER.
YOU'RE UPSET. I CAN UNDERSTAND THAT.
GET OUT AND STAY OUT, MISTER.
SLAM
IT'S OKAY... IT'S OKAY...
...I'M GONNA GET YOU OUT OF HERE...

STEEL MILL -- WILMINGTON...
...SPECIAL AGENT STERN, FBI.
YOU'RE CLEAR TO PROCEED, MS. STERN.
POLICE LINE DO NOT CROSS POLICE L
KARYN STERN, SPECIAL OPERATIONS EXECUTIVE, SIMI VALLEY PROJECT. IT'S TWENTY TWO HUNDRED AND I'VE JUST RETURNED TO THE WILMINGTON SITE FOR A FINAL CHECK.
WHILE WE AWAIT AGENT SPASKY'S REPORT ON THE DYSONS AND THE LAB SPECS ON THE RECOVERED EVIDENCE, I HAVE DECIDED TO INSPECT THE MILL ONCE MORE BE-FORE IT IS CLEARED AND RE-OPENED.
KLIK

THE GRADE TWO LIMB SEGMENT WAS RECOVERED FROM THE MILL ASSEMBLY HERE, AT POINT ALPHA BRAVO ON THE SCHEMATICS.
NOTE THAT THE MILL OWNERS ARE TO BE REIMBURSED FOR THE DISMANTLING COSTS.
POLICE
NOT CROSS POLICE
DO NOT CROSS

I... I CAN ALMOST FEEL IT HERE, TRAPPED, CRUSHED, TRYING TO GET FREE.
I WONDER IF IT FELT PAIN AS IT TORE ITSELF LOOSE?

STRIKE THAT! OF COURSE IT DIDN'T!
I'VE STUDIED THIS STUFF LONG ENOUGH TO KNOW THAT THE SENSORY RELAYS ARE PROBABLY SIGNIFICANTLY INFERIOR TO HUMAN NEURAL SYSTEMS.

WE'VE SAMPLE-TESTED ALL AROUND THE SITE. PERHAPS SOMETHING ELSE WILL TURN UP.
AN INITIAL SCLEROGRAPHIC ASSAY HAS SHOWN UNUSUAL ALLOYS IN THIS SMELTING VAT... THAT'S POINT ALPHA LIMA ON THE PLANS.
DO NOT CROSS
LEFT OF POINT ALPHA LIMA IS--
ODD. THERE SEEMS TO BE A '94 PONTIAC ON THE LOADING DOCK. CALIFORNIA PLATES. I DON'T REMEMBER THAT BEING THERE BEFORE ...
IT'S MINE.
WHO THE--
NO! Oh NO!
SSSH-CHUK!
THAT WAS QUICK.
NOT CROSS
THERE WAS NOTHING TO SEE.

The hotel stays tight till dawn. We sleep in the car.
I'm starting to have second thoughts about this. I want to see the Dysons again. I need to. But I can't risk exposure to the authorities.
PARKING
Maybe we should cut our losses here. It's a long drive to the mountains.
mmmnnnhh
W'TIME'SIT?
EARLY.
WHERE ARE YOU GOING?
STRETCH MY LEGS. SCOPE AROUND.
DON'T SWEAT IT, MOM.
I want to stop him, but I know I shouldn't.
John's life is his own, no matter what. If I suffocate him with protection, I'll be doing him no favors in the days that might come.
And I won't be here to watch over him forever.
He's got to make his own choices. He's got to make his own future.
2.00

WELCOME
WELCOME
LONG NIGHT eh, SUCKER?
"Check this. Sleeping Beauty" he mouths at me.
GIVE ME STRENGTH...
STAIRS
HELLO? WAKE UP CALL...
YEEECK
Huh?

HEY!
Oh MY GOD! YOU!
THERE! THERE THEY ARE, FOR GOD'S SAKE!
DING!
Oh MAN!
What's he doing in there? What's taking so long?
STOP! HOLD IT THERE! YOU HEAR ME, LADY?
COME ON! IT'S CHECK OUT TIME!
Oh GOD! Oh GOD!
MOMMY? MOMMY?

STOP THEM!
WHAT THE HECK--?
HOLY--!
FRUNTCHHH!
WHOA! BRUTAL!
SCREEEEEEE-KKK!
HEY...
...LIBERTYVILLE?
GET IN!
CONNOR! IT'S CONNOR!

I DO NOT BELIEVE THIS! WHAT ARE YOU? TRANQUILIZED?
...COULDA KILLED ME...
SHE SHOULDA, YOU WASTE OF SPACE! GET OUT OF THE WAY!
SPASKY TO OPERATIONS! WE HAVE THREE ABSCONDING WITNESSES SOUTHBOUND ON WESTERN! BACK UP REQUESTED!
ROGER, AGENT SPASKY. AM SHOWING YOU IN PURSUIT.
PUT THE CALL OUT ON THE POLICE BAND! WE'LL NEED ASSIST CUTTING THEM OFF!
ADVISE ALL ELEMENTS THAT SARAH CONNOR IS WITH THE ABSCONDEES. POST HER AS DANGEROUS AND ARMED.
I... JUST WANTED TO GET OUT OF THERE. I COULDN'T STAND THEIR QUESTIONS ANYMORE.
I CAN'T BELIEVE YOU WERE JUST THERE LIKE THAT...
HEY, TIMING IS OUR SPECIALTY.
THEY'RE ON US. CLOSING.
YEAH. DRAG.
Oh LORD. WHAT WILL THEY DO WITH US WHEN THEY CATCH US?
THEY WON'T CATCH US.

THANKS.
HAVE A NICE ONE.

HEY, MAN. YOUR BUDDY WANTS YOU.
WHAT?
MOSSBERG! MOSSBERG! GET YOUR BUTT OVER HERE!

WHAT'S GOING ON?
GET IN! IT JUST CAME OVER THE AIR!

WHAT DID?
CONNOR!
POSITIVE MAKE AND ONLY EIGHT BLOCKS AWAY. THEY'RE CALLING DOWN EVERYTHING ON HER, BUT WE'RE CLOSE.
...REPEAT, ALL UNITS. SUSPECT SOUTHBOUND ON WESTERN. '90 GREEN NISSAN PATHFINDER. ASSISTANCE REQUESTED...

...SUSPECT SARAH CONNOR, WANTED IN CONNECTION WITH A CODE 999 AT IRVINE THURSDAY. SUSPECT REPORTED AS ARMED AND DANGEROUS. PROCEED WITH CAUTION...
REALISTIC

...REPEAT, ALL UNITS. SUSPECT SOUTHBOUND ON WESTERN...

SKREE
HOLD ON.
Oh MY GOD!
SHEEK!

Oh F--

WHUUNNNGHH

TOO FAST!
DID YA SEE?
CRAZY MAN
DAMN! DAMN! DAMN!
WHAT'S YOUR GAME, ASSHOLE?

WHCHK!
EHGG!
GET OUT OF MY LIFE, PINHEAD.
SPASKY TO OPERATIONS. I'M OUT OF THE CHASE! FOR GOD'S SAKE, GET THE LOCAL GEEKS TO CUT HER OFF AT WASHINGTON BEFORE SHE MAKES THE INTERSTATE.
UNDERSTOOD...

WEEOOOOEEOOO
AW NUTS! NOW WE GOT COPS!
WEEOOOOEEOOO
EEEOOOOEEOO
I SEE THEM, JOHN.
ARE YOU STRAPPED IN?
Oh PLEASE!
REALITY CHECK, MOTHER. "FATE OF THE WORLD?" "ROAD SAFETY?" WHAT'S WRONG WITH THIS PICTURE?
EVERYTHING. TRUST ME.
THUMP
AAAAIIGH!
SHOOT!
POLICE
EEEERRRRRKKKK

BACK! BACK IT UP!
WAY COOL...
...WAY, WAY COOL.
YOU LIKED THAT, huh?
...GONNA KILL US ALL. YOU'RE GONNA KILL US ALL...
...YOU KILLED MILES AND NOW YOU'RE GONNA--
Oh MY GOD! Oh MY GOD! AHEAD OF US! AHEAD OF US!
MOM!
DAMN!
SARAH! SARAH CONNOR!
SKREEEEEEEEL!
WEATHERBY, L.A.P.D.! DON'T DO ANYTHING CRAZY, SARAH! I WANT TO HELP YOU!
Trapped. Cruisers closing behind, plain clothes in front.
I was enjoying this too much. I was stupid.
And we're all going to pay the price.
Unless...

OUT OF THE WAY! NOW!
DON'T DO THIS, SARAH! I WANT TO HELP! PLEASE!
MOM! NO! THEY'RE JUST COPS!
I SAID BACK!
DON'T YOU REMEMBER ME, SARAH? I CAME TO SEE YOU AT PESCADERO! ABOUT THE TERMINATORS!
SHLKK
ENOUGH, MAN! LEAVE IT!
I BELIEVE, SARAH! I BELIEVE THEY EXIST! I WANT TO HELP YOU!
TRUST ME! I'LL CALL THE UNIFORMS OFF! I'LL GET IMMUNITY FOR YOU!
I'VE HEARD THAT TOO MANY TIMES BEFORE!
DON'T MAKE ME HURT YOU, WEATHERBY.
PLEASE, SARAH...
WHAT CAN I DO TO MAKE YOU BELIEVE ME?
BOOM BOOM BOOM
BUHHKK--!

He falls. He dies. And before I even see why, I know why.
GOD HELP ME...
It wasn't over.
We didn't win.
It's back.
SARAH CONNOR ...
FOOOM
FOOOM
BABOOOOM!
NISSAN
NEXT:
JUDGMENT IMPAIRED

TERMINATOR® 2 JUDGMENT DAY
CYBERNETIC DAWN

It's back.
I hoped. I prayed. I fought. But it's back.
Third time's a charm.
Dan Abnett writer •
Rod Whigham penciller •
Jack Snider inker •
Patrick Owsley letterer •
Shannon Blanchard color design •
Malibu Color interior color •
Dan Shaheen editor •
Rod Whigham & Chuck Maiden cover art •
story by Dan Abnett Mark Paniccia & Gerry Kline
JUDGMENT IMPAIRED
TERMINATOR® 2: JUDGMENT DAY

JOHN! JOHN! GET DOWN! STAY DOWN!
Weatherby. Did he mean it when he said he believed me?
Moot point, now walking proof has shot him dead.
I try to catch his partner's eye...
...no joy. All he can see is his friend's butchered corpse.
BRAAAKK
It's out of ammo.
Three seconds to reload, tops.
Chkk-
Chk

Make them count.
BLAMM
BAMM
BLAMM
BAMM
But they don't. They never do. There's never enough time.
SHLAKK
WHAT?!
CHKK!
WHHUNNCH!
SKREEEEEEEE

CONNOR! COME ON! COME ON, DAMMIT!
MOM?
GO! GO! GO! MOVE IT!
Oh MY GOD! Oh MY GOD!
DRIVE! DRIVE!
SHREEEEEEEEE
...REPEAT! OFFICER DOWN! MULTIPLE GUNSH--
Oh MY GOD! CHECK THIS OUT!

SCANNING
9004 46
5774 00
2554 61
5721 44
4571 99
0034 76
04992
48299
59285
28850
27499
00371
28778
SEARCH MODE
DROP IT! DROP IT NOW!
STOP! POLICE!
BAM
BAM
BAM
AGHH!
AYKK!
SHREEEEEE

WHAT'S YOUR NAME?
MOSSBERG.
THAT WAS FAST THINKING BACK THERE, MOSSBERG, BUT WE'LL HAVE TO DO MORE IF WE'RE GOING TO STAY ALIVE.
THAT WAS... ONE OF THOSE *THINGS*, WASN'T IT? LIKE WEATHERBY SAID.
RIGHT.
Oh JESUS.
KEEP IT TOGETHER! IT'S IN THE CRUISER BEHIND US AND IT'S CLOSING.
I NEED YOU *SHARP*, MOSSBERG!
MOM!
AHHH!
B-LAM!

THERE! THERE! THE CONSTRUCTION SITE!
EVANS CONSTRUCTION
OKAY!
WHHUNNCHHKK!
COME ON! STAY TOGETHER! THROUGH TO THE LEFT!
WE'RE DEAD!
NO ONE DIES TILL I TELL THEM THEY CAN!

SIMI VALLEY, CALIFORNIA.
EARLY START TODAY, MS. STERN?
NetWork DEVELOPMENTS
THAT'S RIGHT.
HAVE A NICE ONE.
THANKS. YOU TOO.
NW SECURITY
KARYN STERN SPEAKING.
KARYN! IT'S SPASKY! GET A LOAD OF THIS!
IT'S CONNOR! SHE SPRUNG THE DYSONS FROM THE SAFE HOUSE LOCATION!
BRRRP!
WHERE ARE YOU?
IN PURSUIT! BUT THERE'S MORE! I THINK WE HAVE A FUNCTIONING UNIT DOWN HERE AFTER THEM!
SOMETHING TOOK THE COP APART TO GET AT CONNOR! I MEAN, IT, KARYN! A LIVE ONE! I'VE GOT SPECIAL OPS COMING IN TO BACK ME UP!
DID YOU HEAR ME, KARYN? A LIVE ONE!
I HEARD YOU.
KEEP ME INFORMED.

THWMMP!
'BUD'
One thing I've learned through all of this.
You can only run so far.
Running just gets you tired and delays the inevitable.
The only way to live is to turn and fight.

OVER HERE, YOU SON OF A BITCH!
BAMM! BAMM! BLAMM!
BOOOM!
GAAAH!
THUNNK!
Oh
GOD
HELP
HAIL MARY, FULL OF GRACE ...

BRRMMMFFF!
BRRRMMMFMMMMCHH!
WHMMCH!
COME ON!
COME ON!
KLNNG-GGNNCH!

NOOO!

KRUNTCHHH!

Y-YOU KILLED IT.
WASN'T EVER ALIVE.
STAY BACK. THE POWER CORE IS HOUSED IN THE CHEST, SO IT'S PROBABLY SCRAGGED, BUT YOU CAN'T TAKE A CHANCE WITH THESE BASTARDS.
SO LET'S GO! GET OUT OF HERE!
WE CAN'T LEAVE IT HERE.
WHAT? LIKE HELL WE CAN'T!
JOHN'S RIGHT.
I'M ALWAYS RIGHT...
IF WE DITCH IT AND IT ISN'T DEAD, WE'LL HAVE SUCKERED OURSELVES.
AND AFTER THE TROUBLE WE WENT THROUGH AT CYBERDYNE, WE CAN'T LEAVE IT HERE TO BE FOUND.
BUT IT MUST WEIGH HALF A TON...!
THEN WE TAKE WHAT REALLY MATTERS...

CAREFUL!
DON'T HAVE A COW, MOM. JUST WATCH THE EYES. IF YOU SEE RED...
...JOHN'S DEAD.
YES! AND THE CROWD GOES WILD!
CHAKK
AND FOR MY NEXT TRICK!
THAT'S ENOUGH, JOHN.
KEEP IT SAFE. NOW LET'S MOVE.
WHERE D'YOU LEARN TO DO THAT?
MY UNCLE SHOWED ME HOW.
The terminator's CPU was the one thing we couldn't let the authorities have.
Working with only a damaged version, Miles Dyson had all but constructed the basis of Skynet. And then he gave his life to stop that from happening.
But everything we won that night at Cyberdyne seems to have been lost again. This terminator is proof that the Skynet future is still fact.
Despite the immediate threat of the sirens yowling in the streets outside, hunting for us, I need to know why.

INSIDE NETWORK DEVELOPMENTS...
YOU'LL HURT YOUR EYES, KARYN.
WHAT?
YOU'RE SCROLLING THE SCREEN SO *FAST*, YOU'LL HURT YOUR EYES.
YOU CAN'T BE TAKING ANYTHING IN.
NO, OF COURSE NOT.
I'M JUST... *THINKING*.
KARYN! I'VE GOT SPASKY ON LINE FIVE!
PICK UP QUICK! HE SOUNDS LIKE HE'S GONNA HAVE A CORONARY!
SPASKY?
KARYN! I'M WITH SPECIAL OPS AT A CONSTRUCTION SITE OFF FAIRFAX!
WE'VE GOT ONE!

IT'S TAKEN A POUNDING, BUT EVERTHING SEEMS TO BE HERE! IT'S STILL GOT PARTS OF THE SYNTHETIC FLESH ATTACHED!
RETRIEVAL IS BAGGING IT UP RIGHT NOW! GET AN INSPECTION SUITE READY TO RECEIVE!
KARYN, THIS IS INCREDIBLE!
THE COPS ARE GOING MAD BECAUSE I WON'T LET THEM INTO THE SCENE! CAN YOU GET ON THE HORN TO CITY HALL AND PULL RANK?
OF COURSE.
EXPECT US IN TWO HOURS.
GOOD NEWS?
UM, YES. GOOD NEWS.

We go to ground in a motel on the interstate.
Running any further in daylight would leave us wide open to the authorities.
Now we have a chance to piece things together.
.. ...THE FEDS WERE ALL OVER THE MILL. WEATHERBY GOT INSIDE. HE SAW... AN ARM, WEDGED IN SOME GEARS.
THAT WAS WHAT... CONVINCED HIM.
THERE'S GOT TO BE MORE TO IT.
WHAT DO YOU MEAN "MORE"?
THEY COULD LEARN A LOT FROM THE ARM... MECHANICAL SYSTEMS, ALLOYS, PERIPHERAL ELECTRONICS.
BUT NOTHING ABOUT THE MACHINE'S BRAIN. NOTHING THAT COULD LEAD THEM TO SKYNET. SOMETHING ELSE MUST GIVE THEM THE EDGE...
A-ARE YOU SAYING MILES DIED FOR NOTHING?
IS THAT WHAT YOU'RE SAYING?!?
EASY! TAKE IT EASY!
C'MON, LADY, PLEASE.

HOW MUCH DO YOU UNDERSTAND OF THIS, MOSSBERG?
NOT A WHOLE HELL OF A LOT.
THESE ARE ROBOTS. RIGHT? KILLER ROBOTS FROM THE FUTURE?

POSSIBLE FUTURE, BADGE. GET IT RIGHT.
THERE'S A FUTURE OUT THERE RULED BY A GRIEVOUS COMPUTER CALLED SKYNET. A COMPUTER WE CREATE.
IT'S TOTALLY BAD NEWS FOR EVERYONE.
THIS IS WHAT WE KNOW, MOSSBERG-- IN AUGUST 1997, STRATEGIC DEFENSE DECISIONS ARE HANDED OVER TO A MILITARY COMPUTER SYSTEM CALLED SKYNET.
WITHIN WEEKS, IT BECOMES SELF-AWARE, AND OBLITERATES HUMANITY AS A LOGICAL EXTENSION OF ITS PROGRAMMED WILL TO PROTECT ITSELF.

FROM THE ASHES OF GENOCIDE, HUMANITY FIGHTS BACK. EVENTUALLY, HUMANITY WINS, THANKS TO THE LEADERSHIP OF ONE, INSPIRED LEADER.
MY SON, JOHN CONNOR.

HEY, NO AUTOGRAPHS.
THAT'S WHY THE TERMINATORS WERE SENT BACK. TO KILL HIM. TO MAKE SURE HE NEVER EXISTS.
TO MAKE SURE SKYNET WON'T LOSE.

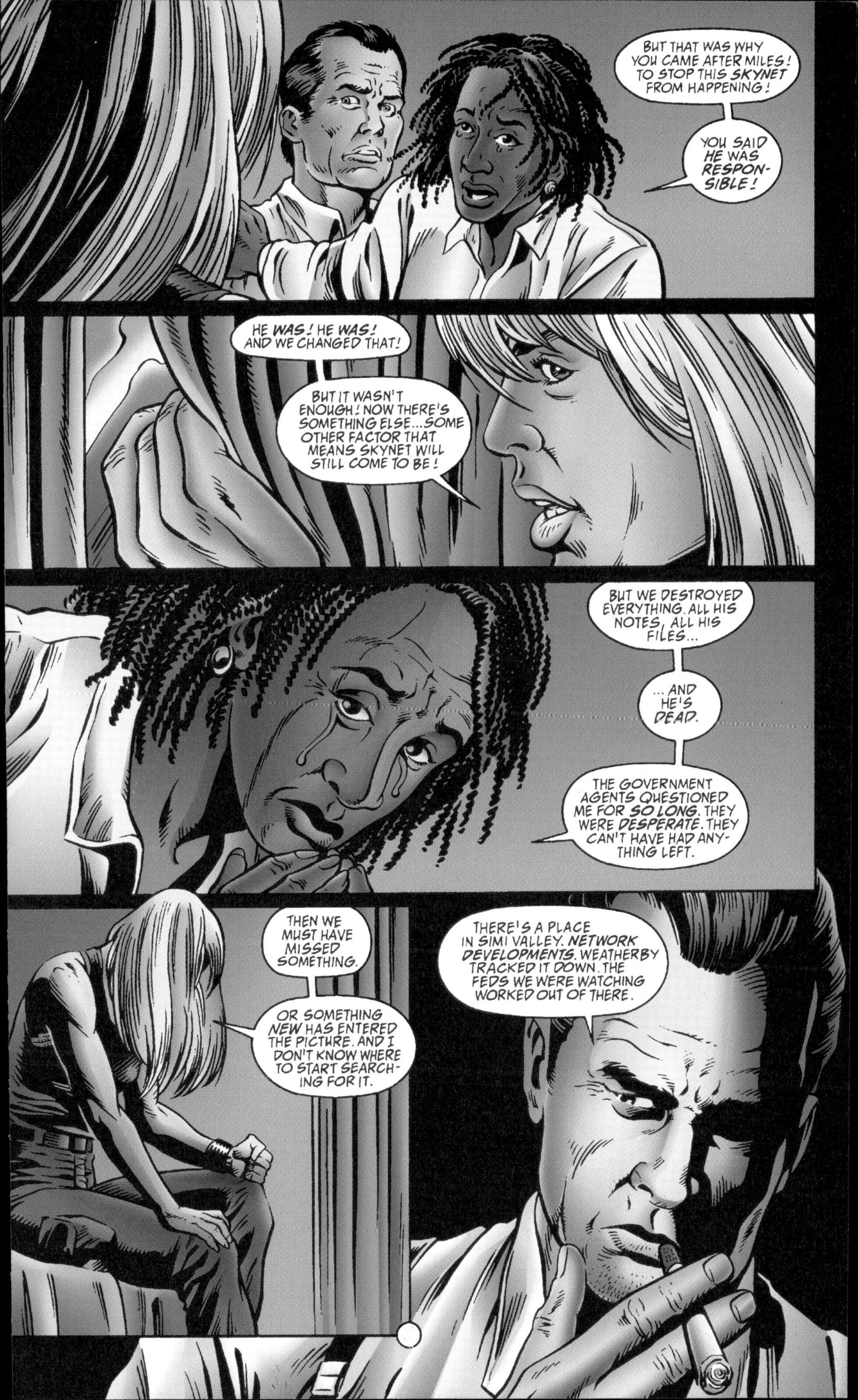
BUT THAT WAS WHY YOU CAME AFTER MILES! TO STOP THIS SKYNET FROM HAPPENING!
YOU SAID HE WAS RESPON-SIBLE!
HE WAS! HE WAS! AND WE CHANGED THAT!
BUT IT WASN'T ENOUGH! NOW THERE'S SOMETHING ELSE...SOME OTHER FACTOR THAT MEANS SKYNET WILL STILL COME TO BE!
BUT WE DESTROYED EVERYTHING. ALL HIS NOTES, ALL HIS FILES...
...AND HE'S DEAD.
THE GOVERNMENT AGENTS QUESTIONED ME FOR SO LONG. THEY WERE DESPERATE. THEY CAN'T HAVE HAD ANY-THING LEFT.
THEN WE MUST HAVE MISSED SOMETHING.
OR SOMETHING NEW HAS ENTERED THE PICTURE. AND I DON'T KNOW WHERE TO START SEARCH-ING FOR IT.
THERE'S A PLACE IN SIMI VALLEY. NETWORK DEVELOPMENTS. WEATHERBY TRACKED IT DOWN. THE FEDS WE WERE WATCHING WORKED OUT OF THERE.

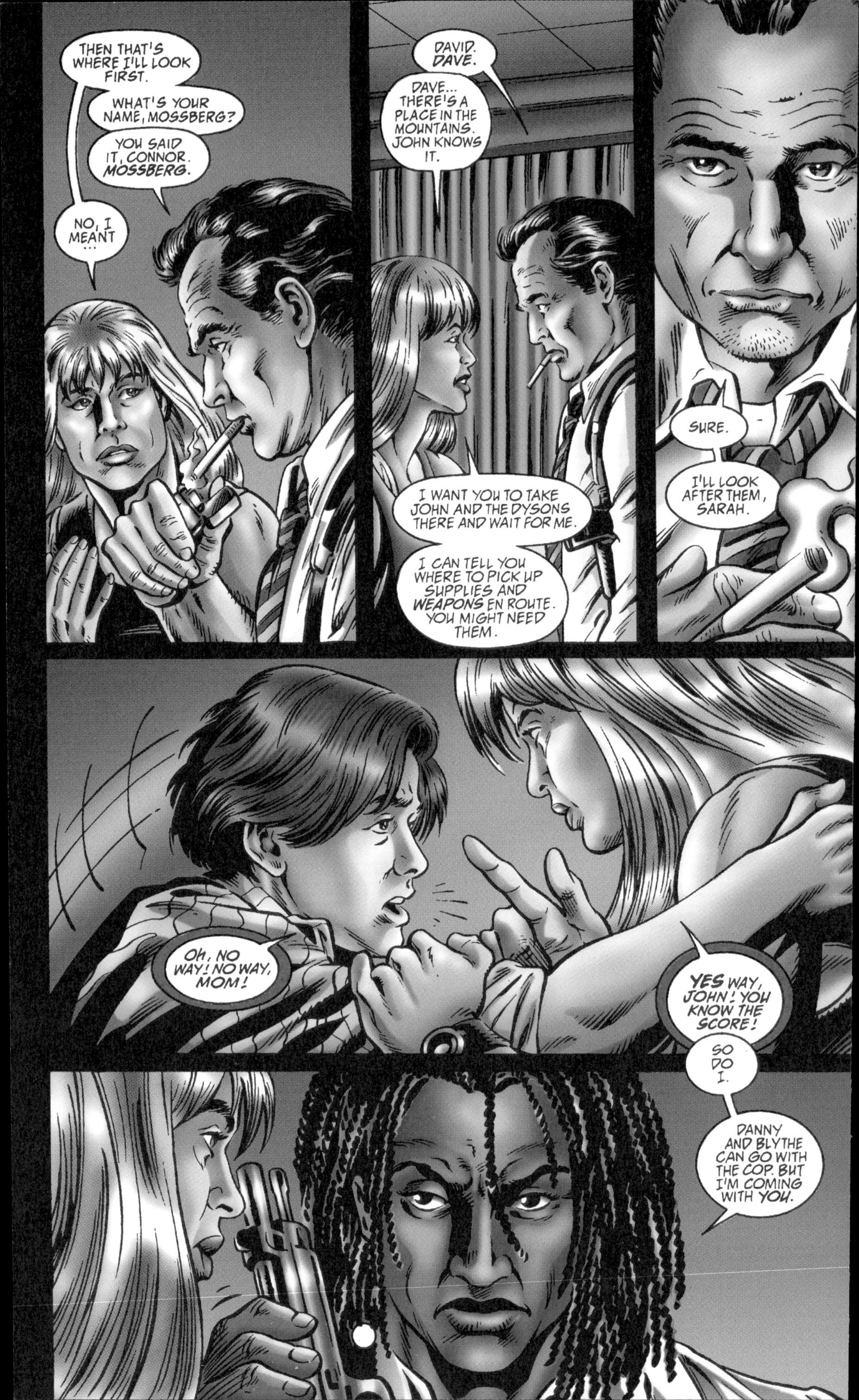
THEN THAT'S WHERE I'LL LOOK FIRST.
WHAT'S YOUR NAME, MOSSBERG?
YOU SAID IT, CONNOR. MOSSBERG.
NO, I MEANT ...
DAVID. DAVE.
DAVE... THERE'S A PLACE IN THE MOUNTAINS. JOHN KNOWS IT.
I WANT YOU TO TAKE JOHN AND THE DYSONS THERE AND WAIT FOR ME.
I CAN TELL YOU WHERE TO PICK UP SUPPLIES AND WEAPONS EN ROUTE. YOU MIGHT NEED THEM.
SURE.
I'LL LOOK AFTER THEM, SARAH.
OH, NO WAY! NO WAY, MOM!
YES WAY, JOHN! YOU KNOW THE SCORE!
SO DO I.
DANNY AND BLYTHE CAN GO WITH THE COP. BUT I'M COMING WITH YOU.

THE SKULL SOCKET'S EMPTY.
YOU CHECKED THE AREA CAREFULLY?
YEAH, NO SIGN.
CONNOR MUST'VE STRIPPED IT OUT AND TAKEN IT. SHE KNOWS HER STUFF.
I'VE GOT ALL AVAILABLE PERSONNEL SEARCHING FOR HER.
LET'S HOPE THEY FIND HER.
SURE.
SHALL I TAKE THIS BABY DOWN TO R&D AND TURN THE BOYS LOOSE ON IT?
YOU DO THAT.
OKAY, LET'S GO!
DEEB
DIP
DIP
DEEB

BREEP
BREEP
BREEP
BREE-
KLK!
YES?
IGGY
CK
OWSLEY
LOS
STRAI
LAURA
TRUCK
STOP
NEXT: GENESIS AND REVELATIONS

TERMINATOR 2

T2™

MALIBU COMICS™ #4

PRESENT WAR

$

TERMINATOR® 2 JUDGMENT DAY

CYBERNETIC DAWN

BNETT • WHIGHAM • SNIDER

CHUCK MAIDEN

EXCUSE ME...

...MY NAME IS *SARAH CONNOR*.

AND I'D LIKE TO SEE WHOEVER'S IN CHARGE HERE.

Dan Abnett • writer
Rod Whigham & Jack Snider • art

Patrick Owsley letterer •
Moose Baumann interior color • & design
Dan Shaheen editor •
Rod Whigham & Chuck Malden cover art •
Story by Dan Abnett & Mark Paniccia

GENESIS & REVELATIONS

TERMINATOR® 2: JUDGMENT DAY

uh
ah
erm
SURELY. JUST A MOMENT.
NEDERMEYER
NETWORK DEVELOPMENTS, SIMI VALLEY, CA.
FINE.
Uh... THIS IS RECEPTION. I HAVE A-- uh-- SARAH CONNOR HERE, WISHING TO SPEAK WITH... WITH SOMEONE IN CHARGE.
YES.
THAT IS CORRECT.
FINE. I'LL DO THAT.
SOMEONE WILL BE DOWN RIGHT AWAY.
THANK YOU.
PLEASE-- uh-- TAKE A SEAT.
WE DON'T HAVE TO GO THAT FAR.

FREEZE! NOT A TWITCH, CONNOR! NOT ONE MOVE!
GET DOWN ON THE FLOOR WITH YOUR HANDS BEHIND YOUR HEAD! NOW!
FAN OUT! SURROUND HER!
oh JESUS!
YOU'RE SPASKY, RIGHT?
YOU'RE THE ONE I WANTED TO SEE.
I CAN TELL YOU NOW, I'M UNARMED.

SHE'S CLEAN.
I TOLD YOU.
SHUT UP!
THIS IS SOME KIND OF TRICK! THE BITCH IS FULL OF DAMN TRICKS!
YOU'VE GOT A NINE TO THE BACK OF MY SKULL, SPASKY.
IF THIS IS A TRICK, IT'S NOT A VERY GOOD ONE, IS IT?

SHE HAS A POINT, SPASKY.
HAVE YOU THOUGHT OF ASKING HER WHAT SHE WANTS?
NO...
WELL, WHY DON'T WE TRY, THEN?
MS. CONNOR? YOUR BUSINESS HERE?

I CAME HERE...
...TO TALK.

HIGHWAY 78, SKIRTING THE CHOCOLATE MOUNTAINS...
THAT EVERYTHING?
POP'S
VIDEO
GIMME SIXTY FILTERLESS. AND I'LL TAKE A COUPLA THESE COMIC BOOKS.
TRAVEL-LING WITH KIDS, HUH?
THE COMICS GAVE IT AWAY, RIGHT?
POP'S
PICKLED EGGS
KISS ME I'M IRISH
MARKERS
50¢
GUM
OIL
VIDEO
NOPE. THE NICOTINE INTAKE.
YOU GOT FAR TO GO?
HAFASS COMICS
MUTATE OR DIE!
YEAH, WE--
--WE GOT A... A LONG WAY TO RIDE YET.
HEY NOW, I AIN'T PRYING NONE, YOUNG FELLA!
I WAS JUST MAKING CONVERSATION IS ALL.
SURE, SURE. I'M SORRY.
LOOK, I'LL GET SOME OF THOSE MAR-KER PENS TOO. YOU GOT ANY SKETCH PADS? KIDS LIKE TO DRAW, RIGHT?
MARKERS 75¢

WHAT'S THAT STUFF HE'S BUYING?
AH-DUH? WHAT DOES HE WANT PENS FOR?
THAT GUY IS SUCH A LOSER.
HE'S OKAY.
HE'S A PRIZE-WINNING WAD, BLYTHE. AND A BADGE TO BOOT.
I CAN'T BELIEVE MOM SADDLED ME WITH HIM.
US.
Huh?
SADDLED US. ALL OF US. YOU, ME AND DANNY. WE'RE A TEAM, MR. MOSSBERG SAID.
DID HE? Pheeeww! WHAT IS HE ON?
HEY, DANNY! WHA'CHA DOING?
DOING?
N-NUTHIN'.
YOU BETTER NOT HAVE WHAT I THINK YOU GOT, SHRIMP!
I AIN'T GOT NUTHIN', JOHN! I SWEAR!
GIVE ME THE C.P.U., DANNY.
YOU HEAR ME, DYSON? GIVE!
GIVE IT TO ME AND I WON'T TELL MOSSBERG YOU WERE FOOLIN' WITH IT, OKAY?

SORR-REE!
I JUST WANTED TO LOOK AT IT...
LEMME SEE IT!
NO!
OKAY, OKAY... I'M SORRY I YELLED. NO HARM DONE.
JUST REMEMBER... THIS THING IS A... A... TERMINATOR'S BRAIN. IT'S THE MOST DANGEROUS THING THERE IS. IF IT GETS LOOSE... THEN THERE'S NO SUCH THING AS A FUTURE FOR ANY OF US.
DON'T CRY, BLYTHE.
I'M NOT.
FOR CHRISSAKES, YOUR DAD DIED KEEPING THIS STUFF SECRET!
WE KNOW.
THAT'S WHY WE'RE HERE.
OKAY, POINT.
TRUCE, YEAH? WHADDYA SAY, CHAMP? HERE COMES MOSSBERG.
SURE. TRUCE.
YOU OKAY BACK THERE? I GOT YOU STUFF... CANDY, COMIC BOOKS, PENS...
THANK GOD! HE GOT US PENS!
WHADDYA KNOW... I DID SOMETHING RIGHT.

Network developments...
INTERVIEW COMMENCES. IT'S EIGHT MINUTES AFTER TEN, FRIDAY THE FIFTH. INTERVIEW SUBJECT SARAH CONNOR HAS SIGNED A RELEASE STATING SHE IS HERE VOLUNTARILY. PRESENT ARE FEDERAL AGENTS KARYN STERN AND VINCENT SPASKY.
SARAH? PERHAPS YOU'D LIKE TO START.
Make or break time. I've come so far, fought so hard, and now it all depends on words.
Here, in the Lion's Den, my toughest fight. If I'm guessing right, there's stuff going on in this building that will somehow ensure the creation of SkyNet.
But a wholesale assault, like the one we staged at Cyberdyne just a few nights ago, would be pointless and doomed.
The only way for me to win here is to be open, and hope that I can persuade them.
Like I convinced Dyson.
Spasky is a no-one. I can see that now. He's a doer, not a thinker, and I can't afford to waste my time on him.
But Stern. I don't know what it is.
She frightens me.
WELL, SARAH?
I CAME HERE, UNARMED, TO TALK, BECAUSE I BELIEVE THAT HONEST COMMUNICATION MIGHT STILL SAVE THE DAMN SPECIES.
I NEED TO KNOW WHAT YOU'RE DOING HERE. TELL ME, AND I'LL SHARE WITH YOU EVERYTHING I KNOW.
BELIEVE ME, YOU CAN'T AFFORD TO HOLD ANYTHING BACK.

DREAM ON, CONNOR! YOU'RE AN ESCAPEE FROM THE PESCADERO NUT-HATCH WHO'S SHOT AND BOMBED HER WAY THROUGH THIS STATE IN DEFIANCE OF THE LAW!
WE'RE REQUIRED TO TELL YOU PRECISELY SQUAT.
VINCENT'S RIGHT, SARAH. YOU HAVE A HISTORY OF PSYCHOTIC EPISODES AND A VERY VIOLENT TRACK RECORD. CAN YOU GIVE US ANY REASON TO EXCHANGE INFORMATION WITH YOU?
ONE-- WE BOTH KNOW ABOUT THE EXISTENCE OF THE MACHINES CALLED TERMINATORS.
TWO-- WE BOTH KNOW THAT THEY REPRESENT A SCENARIO FAR MORE SIGNIFICANT THAN OUR PETTY BICKERING.
THREE-- IF I DON'T WALK OUT OF HERE BY FOUR O'CLOCK THIS AFTERNOON, A PREPARED STATEMENT COVERING EVERYTHING I KNOW ABOUT TERMINATORS COMPLETE WITH CORROBORATING POLICE RECORDS AND DETAILS OF YOUR COMPLICITY, WILL BE DISSEMINATED TO THE MEDIA BY MAIL, FAX AND INTERNET.
YOU'D NEVER CONTAIN IT ALL. IT WOULD BLOW THIS OPERATION WIDE OPEN.
YOU LITTLE--
SPASKY!
VERY THOROUGH MS. CONNOR, BUT WILL ANYONE BELIEVE THE WORD OF AN ESCAPED MENTAL PATIENT?
TOUCHÉ SARAH, BUT IT WOULD TAKE AN AWFUL LOT OF ORGANIZATION TO GUARANTEE SUCH COVERAGE.
GIVEN THE CURRENT STATE OF THE MEDIA, CAN YOU AFFORD TO TAKE THAT CHANCE?
DON'T YOU THINK I'M CAPABLE?

IT'S NOT THAT--
YOUR CELL-PHONE, PLEASE.
WHAT?
GIVE IT TO HER!
OKAY...
THIS IS CONNOR.
I'M IN POSITION.
I'M HANDING YOU OVER NOW.
WELL?
BUT--!?
GO AHEAD. WHO IS THIS?

TARISSA DYSON.
I HAVE SIXTY-FOUR COMMUNIQUES READY FOR DISPATCH VIA EXPRESS POST, FAX AND INTO THREE THOUSAND SEPARATE WEB-SITES ON THE NET.
THEY WILL BE SENT UNLESS I COUNTERMAND THE AUTHORIZATION BEFORE FOUR PM.
DO YOU UNDERSTAND?
PHONE
PHONE
OWSLEY
LEVINE
SHAHEEN
TPC
IGGY
DINGO 91
BOINGO
COIL
71 SEPL
KEEP
L.A.
CLEAN
USING THE DYSON WIDOW IS A NICE TOUCH.
THANK YOU.
BY THE WAY, SPASKY... DON'T BOTHER RUSHING OUT TO TRACE THAT NUMBER BY THE RE-CALL ON YOUR MOBILE...
... IT'S A PAYPHONE ON SEPULVEDA. TARISSA'S ALREADY GONE.
SO...
... WHERE DOES THAT LEAVE US?
WE'D BETTER SHOW YOU AROUND THEN, SARAH.
THIS WAY...
I CAN'T BELIEVE Y--
Oh, BE QUIET, SPASKY.
SARAH?

COOL.
YOU THINK?
YEAH. YOU REMEMBERED IT WELL.
Gee, LIKE I'M GONNA FORGET.
YOU OKAY BACK THERE, KIDS? GREAT VIEW Huh?
Y-huh!
"GREAT VIEW"...
He-he hee!
JOHN...?
YEAH?
I WAS THINKING... THIS COMPUTER... SKYNET...
WHAT ABOUT IT?

THAT CPU IS A BRAIN, RIGHT? AND BRAINS CAN BE MESSED UP BY DISEASES AND STUFF, RIGHT?
LIKE A VIRUS?
YEAH. VIRUSES CAN KILL COMPUTERS, CAN'T THEY?
MY DAD TOLD ME.
YEAH. SO WHAT?
SO COULDN'T WE KILL SKYNET THAT WAY?
RIGHT.
I MEAN IT, JOHN. SKYNET'S BASIC SOURCE CODE HAS TO BE IN THAT CPU SOMEWHERE...
...THAT'S ALL WE'D NEED. THAT, AND ABOUT A MILLION HOURS OF PROGRAMMING.
YOU SERIOUS, DYSON-BRAT?
DEADLY.
WE COULD DO IT, Y'KNOW.
I COULD DO IT.
ONE DAY I'LL HOLD YOU TO THAT, CHAMP!
HE-E-EY!

PLAY NICE, YOU TWO! Y'HEAR?
OKAY, BADGE.
AND DON'T CALL ME THAT.
Oh
Oh MAN
WHERE'D THAT BASTARD COME FROM?
WHAT BASTARD?
MOSSBERG? BADGE?
Oh, PLEASE DON'T TALK THAT WAY, HONEY! YOUR MOM'LL KILL ME!
WHAT IS IT?
BACK THERE, ON THE HOG. SEE HIM?
YEAH.
BASTARD--BASTARD--BASTARD--BASTARD...
SHUT UP, WILL YA! I TOLD YA! F'R CHRISSAKES, I TOLD YA ONCE!
Ah, DON'T CRY, HONEY! PLEASE! I DIDN'T MEAN IT!
oh--uh--uh--uh--uh!
I MEAN THIS, BADGE...
...FLOOR IT, FOR GOD'S SAKE... DRIVE!

BRRRRTTT TTTTT

BRATTISH!
GET DOWN!
POCK! WHUKK!
MOSSBERG!
Oh CHRIST!
HOW DID IT FIND US? HOW DID IT FIND US?!
BRTTTTT
MOSSBERG! WHICH BAG IS YOUR PIECE IN?
DANNO? DANNO?
Ohhh! Ohhh!
IT HURTS ...
DANNY'S HIT! DANNY'S HIT!
Oh YOU SON OF A BITCH!

WHAMMMCHUKK!
YOU DIDN'T HAVE TO SHOOT THE KID!
I GOT HIM! I GOT HIM, RIGHT?
I DUNNO, BADGE! I DIDN'T SEE HIM FALL!
SHRAAKKKTCHH!
NO!
AIIEEE!
HOLY S--

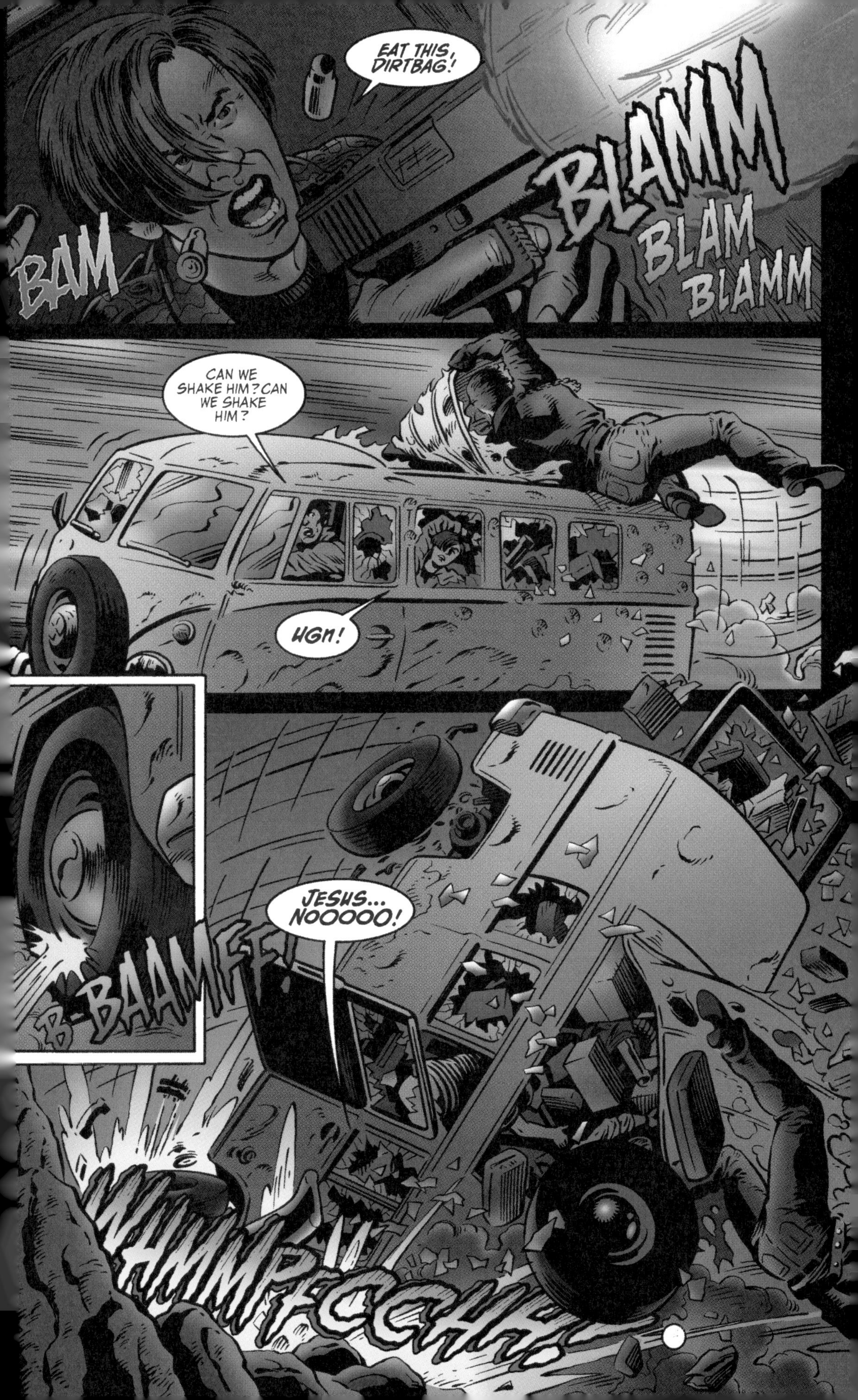
EAT THIS, DIRTBAG!
BAM
BLAMM
BLAM
BLAMM
CAN WE SHAKE HIM? CAN WE SHAKE HIM?
UGn!
JESUS... NOOOOO!
B-BAAMF!
WHAMMPCCHH!

MEANWHILE, BACK AT NETWORK...
OH MY GOD.
I TAKE IT YOU WEREN'T EXPECTING THIS?
SO... MANY.
WHERE DID THEY ALL COME FROM?
15
16
WE THOUGHT YOU KNEW, SARAH.
THE SAME PLACE AS THE ONES THAT ALLEGEDLY STALKED YOU.
THE FUTURE.
BUT--

--WHY SO MANY?
GUINEA PIGS IS OUR GUESS. THESE UNITS HAVE BEEN RECOVERED BY THE U.S. GOVERNMENT FROM SITES ALL AROUND THE WORLD. THE FIRST WAS FOUND IN ARGENTINA IN THE MID-SEVENTIES.
IN TWO DECADES, WE'VE FOUND TWENTY-SEVEN OF THEM.
WE THINK THE CHINESE HAVE ANOTHER THREE, AND THE FRENCH MAY ALSO HAVE ONE.
NONE HAVE BEEN FOUND FUNCTIONING. NONE OF THEM SURVIVED THEIR TRIP HERE. IT CLEARLY TOOK THEIR MANUFACTURER A LONG TIME TO GET THE MEANS OF TRANSPORTATION TO WORK.
THEY HAVE BEEN THE SUBJECT OF INTENSIVE RESEARCH FOR YEARS. THE VALUE OF THE DERIVED TECHNOLOGY CANNOT BE MEASURED.
BUT WE'D ALWAYS PRAYED FOR ONE TO SURVIVE THE TRANSIT EXPERIENCE AND ARRIVE INTACT, SO THAT WE COULD EXAMINE ITS FUNCTION, ITS LIFE, ITS BRAIN...
OF COURSE, WE HAD NO IDEA WHERE THEY CAME FROM OR HOW OR WHY... UNTIL YOU CAME ALONG WITH THOSE ANSWERS.
YOU'VE GOT TO STOP. YOU'VE GOT TO STOP THIS RIGHT NOW.
YOU HAVE NO IDEA WHAT YOU'RE DOING! THIS IS WHY WE DESTROYED CYBERDYNE! THIS IS WHY DYSON DIED!
THESE... THINGS AREN'T SOME LUCKY BREAK... A SHORT CUT TO NEXT YEAR'S TECHNOLOGY.
THEY'RE THE HERALDS OF DESTRUCTION! SKYNET WANTS YOU TO LEARN! IT WANTS YOU TO LEARN SO THAT YOU CAN BUILD SKYNET!

Oh, I HAVE HAD IT WITH YOU!
YOU'RE SO OUT OF YOUR DEPTH HERE IT'S EMB--
SPASKY!
GO AND COOL OFF FOR A MINUTE.
SCREAMING ISN'T GOING TO GET US ANYWHERE.
SO, SARAH... YOU CONVINCED MILES DYSON HE WAS MAKING A MISTAKE AND GOT HIM TO DESTROY HIS WORK.
AND NOW YOU WANT TO TALK SOME SIMILAR SENSE INTO US.
I HAVE TO STOP YOU. SKYNET MUST NEVER HAPPEN.
SO YOU SAY.
AND YOU'LL LEAK THIS ALL TO THE MEDIA TONIGHT IF WE DON'T ACQUIESCE AND LET YOU WALK FREE?
YOU KNOW DAMN WELL I WI--
--GOD! NO!

THEN SARAH CONNOR WILL WALK OUT OF HERE THIS AFTERNOON ...
NEXT: NO FATE

TERMINATOR 2

T2

MALIBU COMICS #0

PRESENT WAR

TERMINATOR 2 JUDGMENT DAY

CYBERNETIC DAWN

Reese said... there's no fate but what we make for ourselves.
And that's what they're making here, in a vault in Simi Valley, picking up where Dyson and Cyberdyne left off.
Reverse engineering terminator endoskeletons -- aborted time travelers -- for their secrets...
I tried to stop it. I had to try. And in trying, I found what was directing their insane schemes.
Another polyalloy T-1000.
YUUHNN!
Dan Abnett • writer
Rod Whigham & Jack Snider • art
NO FATE
Patrick Owsley • letterer
Moose Baumann • color design
Malibu Color • interior color
Dan Shaheen • editor
Rod Whigam & Joel Naprstek • cover art
Story by Dan Abnett & Mark Paniccia
TERMINATOR 2: JUDGMENT DAY
If there ever was a real Dr. Karyn Stern, my hopes for success here died with her.
Now it intends to terminate me, to try to assume my identity to get at John and the others.
FRATSHH!
Uhhnn!
The alarms should bring others in here, which could be my only chance.
BREEP
BREEP
EXIT
Unless they're all polyalloy Killers.

STERN! WHAT THE H--
OH MY GOD!
SPASKY! SHOOT IT! EMPTY YOUR CLIP INTO IT AND FALL BACK FAST!
STAY BACK! STAY BACK!
BAM!
CHAM! CHAM-CHAM! CHAM!
gak.
WHUNNCHHH!
Spasky always said he wanted to meet a live one.
Achieving his ambition has bought me vital seconds.
HOLD IT, CONNOR!
WHAT THE HELL'S GOING ON UP HERE?
NO TIME!
THUKK!
BOOOO
EHKK!
WHMMP

SARAH?
YOU CAN'T LEAVE.
BAM
BAM
BAM
SCREW YOU!
BRAAAPPP!
HATT
FPANG!
THUKK
WUK
WUK
WUK
Those chrome wounds will heal in seconds. It's almost unkillable.
The only way to stop a T-1000 is to freeze it or melt it... or do anything which breaks down its structure at a base level to stop it from reconfiguring.
WEEEB
WEEEB
So I need a smart plan. And as many distractions as I can get.

Chem-Analysis Lab. Good start.
EXIT
LAB 7
GET OUT! MOVE!
Just hope I've got time to improvise somethi--
FWKK-
RASSHH-
Guhh!
I give it everything I've got... everything at hand... sample beakers, dropper trays, test molds ... anything not bolted down.
BRAKAKTT!
TSHH!
STRASHH
F-TSHH
And just when the H&K runs out, fate steps in.
One flask out of hundreds. A solvent. The label on the broken bottle says 27B/6.
It freezes the upper layers of the polyalloy like ice on a pond.

Maybe it makes the alloy inert. Maybe it wipes the molecular programming. Maybe it's only temporary, but it works for now.
CHEMICAL
All I know for sure is that I need a **hell** of a lot more of it.
27B/6... 27B/6...
27B/6
MGFF-AHHHH!
27B/6
SKRRUKKK
SPPSSHHH!

YYEEEEEHHHFGHG
It spasms and lashes as it dies. Flailing limbs rupture other drums and an acrid stink rises as chemicals intermix in dangerous proportions.
I don't look back.
Dry burn. Ignition. Fireball. Hammerblow.
Thank god the fire drill had gotten the staff out.
FWHOOMF!
Everything burns. Everything they had.
Except perhaps that human imperati to invent for invention's sake. Ste and Spasky followed Dyson. Who'll follow them?
Some damn fool, you can be certain.

We're right back where we started, John.
We still can't be sure if we've won.
HIGHWAY 78, CROSSING THE CHOCOLATE MOUNTAINS...
BLYTHE! BLYTHE!
COME ON! WE HAVE TO HELP DANNY!
BLYTHE DYSON! GET OVER HERE!
RING AROUND THE ROSIE. POCKET FULL OF POSIES. ASHES, ASHES, WE ALL FALL DOWN.
DANNY? COME ON, CHAMP! WAKE UP! WAKE UP!
PLEASE, CHAMP, WAKE UP...
MOSSBERG! WHERE ARE YOU? MOSSBERG!
DANNY NEEDS HELP NOW, BADGE!
SKK-RRT-
CHHCHCH-HHH-!
Huh?
OH NO!

gnnh
Hak! Hak! Hak!
JEEEEEEZUS.
MOSSBERG! PLEASE! **PLEASE!**
JOHN?
HANG ON, JOHN. HANG ON.
GOTTA CLEAR MY HEAD. FIND STUFF.
YEAH. THAT'S RIGHT. **STUFF.**
HE-LLO **BABY!**
THIS IS WHAT I NEED. I **THINK.**
HOW **HARD** CAN IT BE?
MOSSBERG! IF YOU'RE GONNA DO SOMETHING ...
...DO IT **QUICK!**

I CAN'T RUN FOREVER, YOU HEAR ME?
MOSSBERG! IT'S ALL OVER ME!
ughhnn!
NO!
Oh GEEZ! NO GOOD!
HANG ON, JOHN! JUST HANG ON!
...STUPID TOGGLE SONUVA...
I CAN'T HANG ON!
OKAY THEN...
...DUCK.

KRAKA
THOOOOOMM!
whaddyaknow...
WAY TO GO, BADGE.

I run. I hide. I make some calls.
Tarissa finds me after midnight.
SARAH? WHAT H--
JUST DRIVE.
How can I tell her the real truth?
How can I tell her that it'll probably start again? The one thing this has showed me is that it's not the Terminators we should really fear.
It's mankind and our terrible ability to survive, an ability we will not lose until we have made sure the machines have inherited it.
While I sort out the terrible implications of these new developments, we go to ground.
The next day, we make the mountains.
rue to his word, David Mossberg has led our children to safety.
And they've had adventures of their own on the way. Our friends the Salcedas have tended Danny Dyson's wounds.
Seems they took out an 800 en route.
I feel obsolete.
LET'S TALK.

I tell him about Network and the T-1000.
I explain to him that I think Skynet is now a certainty. No matter how many times we delay its creation, there will always be someone eager to step in and finish what's been started... just to see if they can.
We are our own worst enemy. The nuclear twilight will come.
SO THE FIGHT MAY LAST AWHILE. AND IT MIGHT GET DIRTIER.
WE WERE KINDA EXPECTING THAT, WEREN'T WE?
IGGY P
DANNY AND I HAVE BEEN THINKING...
He tells me about the source code. He explains Danny's virus idea and his own long-term plan...
...and for a moment, I'm too surprised to be proud of my son.
John is wise enough, even in a battle of astounding odds, to recognize that a child's imagination can be the children of the future.
"There's no fate but what we make for ourselves", he reminds me with a laugh, Kyle's intensity in his eyes.
NO FATE. WE'RE GOING TO MAKE IT OURSELVES WITH THE LIVES OF THREE BILLION PEOPLE, JOHN. IT SEEMS SO INEVITABLE, THE WAR, JUDGMENT DAY... IT CAN'T BE CHANGED. IT'S OUR FUTURE.
IF IT IS INEVITABLE, MOM, THEN IT ALSO MEANS WE'LL WIN... SOMEDAY.
We'll make it.
One way or another.
END

OTHER GRAPHIC NOVELS FROM BOXTREE

TERMINATOR 2
T2®

BOXTREE

FUTURE WAR

TERMINATOR 2® JUDGMENT DAY

NUCLEAR TWILIGHT

BOXTREE

PANICCIA

ERSKINE

GRAPHIC NOVELS

ISBN	Title	Price
☐ 0 7522 0144 1	Barb Wire Movie Adaptation	£6.99 pb
☐ 0 7522 0897 7	Daredevil – man without fear	£9.99 pb
☐ 0 7522 0645 1	Marvels	£10.99 pb
☐ 0 7522 0856 X	Shadow	£6.99 pb
☐ 0 7522 0762 8	Species Movie Tie in	£8.99 pb
ALIENS V PREDATOR		
☐ 0 7522 0878 0	Aliens v Predator – Deadliest of the Species 1	£9.99 pb
☐ 0 7522 0695 8	Aliens v Predator – Deadliest of the Species 2	£9.99 pb
RANMA		
☐ 0 7522 0851 9	Ranma Book 1	£5.99 pb
☐ 0 7522 0861 6	Ranma Book 2	£5.99 pb
SPIDER-MAN		
☐ 0 7522 0385 1	Spiderman: Chance Encounters	£8.99 pb
☐ 0 7522 0123 9	Spiderman: Greatest Villains	£9.99 pb
☐ 0 7522 0107 7	Spiderman: Masques	£6.99 pb
☐ 0 7522 0112 3	Spiderman: Perceptions	£8.99 pb
☐ 0 7522 0808 X	Spiderman: Revenge of the Sinister Six	£8.99 pb
☐ 0 7522 0876 4	Spiderman: Return of the Sinister Six	£9.99 pb
☐ 0 7522 0307 X	Spiderman: Silver Sable	£8.99 pb
STAR TREK DEEP SPACE NINE		
☐ 0 7522 0134 4	Dax's Comet	£8.99 pb
☐ 0 7522 0928 0	Emancipation	£7.99 pb
☐ 0 7522 0933 7	Emancipation and Beyond	£7.99 pb
☐ 0 7522 0898 5	Hearts and Minds	£8.99 pb
☐ 0 7522 0245 6	Maquis	£8.99 pb
☐ 0 7522 0888 8	Requiem	£7.99 pb
☐ 0 7522 0255 3	Shanghaied	£8.99 pb
STAR WARS		
☐ 0 7522 0893 4	Classic Star Wars – A New Hope	£8.99 pb
☐ 0 7522 0913 2	Classic Star Wars	£8.99 pb
☐ 0 7522 0747 4	Classic Star Wars 2	£10.99 pb
☐ 0 7522 0752 0	Classic Star Wars 3	£10.99 pb
☐ 0 7522 0302 9	Star Wars – Boba Fett	£8.99 pb
☐ 0 7522 0987 6	Star Wars – Dark Empire	£9.99 pb
☐ 0 7522 0822 5	Star Wars – Dark Empire 2	£9.99 pb
☐ 0 7522 0616 8	Star Wars – Dark Lords of Sith	£10.99 pb
☐ 0 7522 0804 7	Star Wars – Droids	£8.99 pb
☐ 0 7522 0606 0	Star Wars – Empire Strikes Back	£8.99 pb
☐ 0 7522 0704 0	Star Wars – Jabba the Hutt	£8.99 pb
☐ 0 7522 0611 7	Star Wars – Return of the Jedi	£8.99 pb
☐ 0 7522 0798 9	Star Wars – River of Chaos	£8.99 pb
☐ 0 7522 0817 9	Star Wars – Tales of the Jedi and Freedom Nadd Uprising	£10.99 pb
STREET FIGHTER		
☐ 0 7522 0813 6	Street Fighter II – Book 1	£7.99 pb
☐ 0 7522 0818 7	Street Fighter II – Book 2	£8.99 pb
UNCANNY X MEN		
☐ 0 7522 0151 4	Uncanny X Men: Acts of Vengeance	£8.99 pb
☐ 0 7522 0161 1	Uncanny X Men – Executions 1	£8.99 pb
☐ 0 7522 0117 4	Uncanny X Men – Executions 2	£8.99 pb
X MEN		
☐ 0 7522 0691 5	Ghostrider/Wolverine/Punisher – Hearts of Darkness/Dark Design	£7.99 pb
☐ 0 7522 0108 5	Wolverine: Triumph and Tragedy	£9.99 pb
☐ 0 7522 0892 6	X-Men Adventures	£9.99 pb
☐ 0 7522 0154 9	X-Men: Bishop – The Mountjoy Crisis	£8.99 pb
☐ 1 85283 390 4	X-Men: Brood Trouble in The Big Easy	£5.25 pb
☐ 0 7522 0139 5	X-Men: Cyclops and Phoenix	£8.99 pb
☐ 0 7522 0756 3	X-Men Gambit	£7.99 pb
☐ 0 7522 0356 8	X-Men: Generation X	£8.99 pb
☐ 0 7522 0871 3	X-Men: God loves, Man kills	£5.99 pb
☐ 0 7522 0103 4	X-Men – Rogue	£8.99 pb
☐ 0 7522 0803 9	X-Men: Sabretooth	£6.99 pb
☐ 1 85283 395 5	X-Men: Wolverine	£6.99 pb

All these books are available at your local bookshop or can be ordered direct from the publisher. Just tick the titles you want and fill in the form below.

Prices and availability subject to change without notice.

Boxtree Cash Sales, P.O. Box 11, Falmouth, Cornwall TR10 9EN

Please send a cheque or postal order for the value of the book and add the following for postage and packing:

U.K. including B.F.P.O. – £1.00 for one book plus 50p for the second book, and 30p for each additional book ordered up to a £3.00 maximum.

Overseas including Eire – £2.00 for the first book plus £1.00 for the second book, and 50p for each additional book ordered.

OR please debit this amount from my Access/Visa Card (delete as appropriate).

Card Number ☐☐☐☐☐☐☐☐☐☐☐☐☐☐☐☐

Amount £ ....

Expiry Date ....

Signed ....

Name ....

Address ....